THE FLYING TRAPEZE:
THREE CRISES FOR PHYSICISTS

THE WHIDDEN LECTURES

Series I (January 1956)
The Anatomy of South African Misery
C. W. DE KIEWIET
President, The University of Rochester

Series II (January 1957)
The Evolution of India
VIJAYA LAKSHMI PANDIT
High Commissioner for India to the United Kingdom

Series III (January 1958)
Colonial Élites: Rome, Spain and the Americas
RONALD SYME
Camden Professor of Ancient History, University of Oxford

Series IV (January 1959)
The Hollow Universe
CHARLES DE KONINCK
Professor of the Philosophy of Nature, Laval University

Series V (January 1960)
Three Aspects of Stuart England
SIR GEORGE CLARK
Provost of Oriel College, Oxford, 1947–57

Series VI (January 1961)
New Horizons in Biblical Research
W. F. ALBRIGHT
Oriental Seminary, Johns Hopkins University
(unpublished)

Series VII (January 1962)
The Flying Trapeze: Three Crises for Physicists
J. ROBERT OPPENHEIMER
Director, Institute for Advanced Study, Princeton, New Jersey

Series VIII (January 1963)
Models and Mystery
PROFESSOR THE REVEREND CANON IAN T. RAMSEY
Nolloth Professor of the Philosophy of Religion, University of Oxford

Series IX (January 1964)
The Paradox of Scottish Culture: the Eighteenth Century Experience
DAVID DAICHES
Professor of English, University of Sussex

THE WHIDDEN LECTURES FOR 1962

The Flying Trapeze:
Three Crises for Physicists

J. ROBERT OPPENHEIMER

Director, Institute for Advanced Study
Princeton, New Jersey

LONDON
OXFORD UNIVERSITY PRESS
NEW YORK   TORONTO
1964

Oxford University Press, Amen House, London E.C.4

GLASGOW NEW YORK TORONTO MELBOURNE WELLINGTON
BOMBAY CALCUTTA MADRAS KARACHI LAHORE DACCA
CAPE TOWN SALISBURY NAIROBI IBADAN ACCRA
KUALA LUMPUR HONG KONG

530. 1
Op 5

Printed in Great Britain by The Alden Press Oxford

Foreword

The Whidden Lectures were established in 1954 by E. C. Fox, B.A., LL.D., of Toronto, the senior member of the Board of Governors, to honour the memory of the late Reverend Howard P. Whidden, D.D., LL.D., D.C.L., F.R.S.C., 1871–1952, Chancellor of McMaster University from 1923 to 1941. Their purpose is to help students cross the barriers separating the academic departments of a modern university. The lectures are not restricted as to general theme.

Dr. Whidden was a member of a family resident in Antigonish, N.S., since 1761, after earlier settlement in New England in 1700. Born in Nova Scotia, he was educated at Acadia University, McMaster University, and the University of Chicago, and served as a minister of Baptist churches in Ontario, Manitoba, and Ohio. From 1913 to 1923 he was President of Brandon College in Manitoba, then affiliated with McMaster University, and served in the House of Commons in Ottawa from 1917 to 1921 as the Union Government member for Brandon. Assuming executive responsibility at McMaster in 1923, he directed what was for the University practically a second founding, its transfer to Hamilton in 1930, from Toronto where it had been established in 1887. He is remembered as a man of striking appearance, unusual dignity, effective leadership, ready tolerance, deep Christian conviction, and broad educational outlook.

The seventh series of Whidden Lectures were delivered in January 1962 by the distinguished Director of the Institute for Advanced Study at Princeton, N.J., Dr. J. Robert Oppenheimer.

A graduate of Harvard University who has studied and lectured at Cambridge, Göttingen, Leyden, Zürich, and many other universities abroad as well as in his own country, Dr. Oppenheimer is perhaps best known to the man in the street as the Director of the Los Alamos Scientific Laboratory during the Second World War and subsequently as the Chairman of the General Advisory Committee to the U.S. Atomic Energy Commission. The success of the Los Alamos project in wartime was largely due to his genius and to the inspiration and leadership he gave to his associates. He is, however, more than an atomic physicist. A great humanist who is deeply concerned about man and his survival, he is a versatile scholar of wide interests and deep culture: his early training, indeed, was in the classical languages of ancient Greece and Rome. All who had the privilege of hearing the Whidden Lectures in 1962 will agree that it is difficult to envisage anyone more eminently suitable to deliver them.

E. T. Salmon
Principal of University College
McMaster University

May 1964

Preface

The three lectures, The Flying Trapeze: Three Crises for Physicists, were given by Professor Oppenheimer from only sketchy outline notes, and were recorded. It was a most stimulating experience to hear these lectures, to witness Professor Oppenheimer's occasional search for the precise word, and to notice the wealth of illustrations that sprang to his mind to illuminate each idea. It was a revelation to me when I looked at the word-for-word transcript of the lectures to see that such sparkling addresses, so clear to the listener, contained so many sentences sufficiently involved to make reading difficult. Moreover, the discussion of each of the three crises, Space and Time, Atom and Field, and War and the Nations, did not fall neatly into the time of one lecture, so that Professor Oppenheimer continued the first topic into the second lecture, and the second topic into the third; this caused him to repeat and summarize certain material. It seemed appropriate in a written account to confine each topic to one chapter. This caused me to coalesce some of the material from the end of one lecture and the start of the next; in the process I have discarded very little that was said, but I have altered the order of a few passages.

I hope that this editing has served to make the verbal transcript more readable, without removing any of the flavour of colloquial verve, and careful phraseology, which combined to make the original lectures such an exciting and satisfying experience. At least the reader may be assured that, although they have been occasionally rearranged, all the significant words are Professor Oppenheimer's.

M. A. PRESTON, M.A., PH.D., F.R.S.C.
Professor of Theoretical Physics
McMaster University

Contents

I. Space and Time

This has been a great century in physics, a century of unexpected, profound, and moving discoveries, and of applications that have changed a great deal in the condition of human life. The last years have seen very great progress in the understanding of essential features of life, and I am confident that the years ahead will teach us more than all preceding history of man about how living organisms perform their miraculous functions and about man as a part of nature. We in physics are still engaged in what feels at the moment like a very great intractable struggle to find out the laws of matter, the nature of matter. It is not of that that I want to speak, but of chapters that are to some extent closed, although questions raised by the answers found earlier in the century are still before us, still wide open. I shall, in this and the second lecture, speak of increases in our understanding, changes in our understanding, of the world of nature. In the third lecture I shall speak rather of changes in the human situation brought about by the developments in physics and other sciences.

Our time is marked by the prominence of the sciences. It is marked by very rapid change and very great growth—growth in science, growth in productivity, growth in population, growth in travel, growth in communication. Almost any statistic that you look at shows a sharp curve with a characteristic of doubling in ten or twenty or thirty years. In the case of the sciences, this doubling occurs in about ten years, and there are several quite spectacular figures which mark it. If you think of all those people who devote their lives to studying nature or applying what has been learned in the technical way and call them scientists, then throughout man's history there have been a number of them and of that number about 93 per cent are still living today, so rapidly has the number of people so engaged increased. A friend of mine, in Europe, calculated how fast one of our journals of fundamental physics was growing, and established that if the rate of growth were maintained, then next century the volumes would weigh more than the whole earth. I was called on, not very long ago, by the Scientific Secretary of the Soviet Academy of Sciences, who spent a day with me in Princeton. I believe that his is an important political office, and we talked a little bit about the growth of scientific activity, in which he is engaged as an administrator. I asked him how he saw the future beyond the next five-year plan, say fifty years from now. Without thinking he said, 'Then all of us will be scientists'; the horror of it came over him slowly and he added, 'No, not quite'.

Still, in talking of this as a scientific age and thinking of this as a time remarkably influenced by science, we need, I think, to bear in mind two cautions. One is that we probably have no very good idea today of the range of problems which will be accessible to science. We do not know how much of human behaviour may yield in one way or another to the characteristically objective and often rather unexpected study that is a science, and we may today live in something of an imbalance between what we know of the physical world, what we are beginning to know of the living world, and what we know of the human world. I, however, am deeply con-

2

vinced that the scientific knowledge which may be available about men—not much today—will always be, as is our knowledge of the physical world, very very incomplete and partial, and that the sense of having to live and act in response to tradition, good judgement, and wisdom, which we have now, will not ever be alleviated by any development of the sciences.

I think we need secondly to remember that a great part of the present scene arises not from what we have learned, but by its application in technology. This, in turn, rests on an organization of the economy and to a more limited, but still real, extent on our political arrangements. Neither of these derives from, nor is in any tight way related to, the sciences, because, although the growth of knowledge is largely responsive to human needs, it is not fully so. The existence of terrible and intractable diseases does cause a very wide and intensive study of problems that may be related to the diseases. Problems of agricultural productivity, problems of gadgetry, perhaps most of all problems of military importance stimulate the vigour and increase the support for research. Still it is a profound and necessary truth that the deep things in science are not found because they are useful; they are found because it was possible to find them.

Think of the long centuries in which attempts were made to change mercury into gold because that seemed like a very useful thing to do. These efforts failed and we found how to change mercury into gold by doing other things that had quite different intentions. And so I believe that the availability of instruments, the availability of ideas or concepts—not always but often mathematical—are more likely to determine where great changes occur in our picture of the world than are the requirements of man. Ripeness in science is really all, and ripeness is the ability to do new things and to think new

3

thoughts. The whole field is pervaded by this freedom of choice. You don't sit in front of an insoluble problem for ever. You may sit an awfully long time, and it may even be the right thing to do; but in the end you will be guided not by what it would be practically helpful to learn, but by what it is possible to learn.

I think that to those who are far removed from the life of the sciences, this sometimes appears to be irresponsible. It seems as though having made something potentially pestiferous, like nuclear bombs, we ought to go ahead and find something potentially helpful in getting rid of them. Indeed we ought; but instead it is much more likely that our thoughts will turn to things that are easier to do than that, that are more at hand than that. It is not irresponsibility; it is characteristic of the special way in which one does advance so rapidly in knowledge, for often one may quickly make an irreversible accession to knowledge by establishing an error. Having proved that something is not right, you do not go back to it again; you have learned your lesson. Progress, which in moral and human things is a very elusive word applicable, certainly, to some aspects of our life, but not to all, is an inevitable thing in the sciences. Progress is co-extensive with the existence of the scientific world.

Now the first two of these lectures have to do with just such episodes, where previously held, firmly entrenched errors were with considerable shock and very great grandeur corrected—and in such a way that those errors will not be made again. Moreover, this progress in learning about the world of nature has changed rather profoundly not only what we know of nature, but some of the things that we know about ourselves as knowers. It has changed, to use an old phrase that is beloved of Butterfield, the 'thinking caps' of men, as did the

4

revolutions of the late middle ages and the seventeenth century. I may be wrong, but I share with my colleagues, or with many of them, a strong conviction that this experience is one which we would gladly extend beyond the range of limited technical communities. The experience of seeing how our thought and our words and our ideas have been confined by the limitation of our experience is one which is salutary and is in a certain sense good for a man's morals as well as good for his pleasure. It seems to us that this is an opening up of the human spirit, avoiding its provincialism and narrowness. You may think of the example of what it has meant to all of us to learn over the last centuries how different other cultures could be from our own and still in some real sense be cultures.

Progress of this kind is possible only because it blends two almost contradictory traits. The one is a great love of adventure, so that you look for new things and for changed circumstances, look far into the sky, look close into matter, do all sorts of things that take you away from the familiar human experience. That lies on the one hand, and on the other is a great adherence to such order and clarity as has already been attained. One may describe the latter as a sense of conservatism about not giving up any understanding that has been achieved, so that even though you are about to rewrite Newton you are very very reluctant to move very far away from Newton, and even though you may realize that everything that has been said before in physics is only very partially true, you will fight very hard to keep that partial truth. You will be strong through the tradition, and you will use the tradition in describing the new experience until that point comes when you simply cannot go on with it and you have to make a great break.

Many of the men who have contributed to the great changes

in science have really been very unhappy over what they have been forced to do. Kepler, who loved spheres, discovered ellipses. Planck, with his famous quantum of action, introduced an element of discontinuity into physics, which seemed to him absolutely intolerably strange and ugly. Einstein, who was able to live with the theories of relativity and regretted only very few aspects of them, also contributed to the development of quantum theory; he proposed the idea of light quanta, but never could reconcile himself to the quantum theory logically built up from this basis. And de Broglie, who discovered that there are waves which are associated with material particles, could never reconcile himself to their interpretation as waves which only represented information and not some disturbance in a corporeal medium.

These changes are forced on physicists somewhat reluctantly because we are both traditional and conservative and at the same time a little too adventurous. In our lifetimes we have seen, in a limited area, our beliefs and our experience radically altered—the popular word is revolutionized, but that is not quite right, for they have been deepened and changed, but not completely overthrown. I have the impression that a general awareness of this and a general experience of it may be of some use in dealing with human problems in a time when the world also is changing so very rapidly.

I have in my enterprise tonight and tomorrow very severe limits; one of them is that especially in physics it is often believed that without the mathematical forms one cannot really say what the discoveries are all about. There is a measure of truth in this; the discoveries could probably not have been made without the mathematical forms which give a quick synoptic and luminous way of representing the order that inheres in nature. It is not surprising that mathematics is involved in nature; it is really a requirement of consistency and the one thing that we are all confident of is that nature may be difficult, but she will not be inconsistent. (It is only we who can be that.) But I think that some understanding of the concepts of physics can be conveyed with very limited use of mathematics, and I propose so to restrict myself. You may think of an analogy. It is certainly better to see Hamlet acted, if it is reasonably well acted, than to read it. It was written to be acted, not to be read in a study. Still, if you read it, you have, with good will and imagination and luck, a good deal of feeling for the meaning of the play. It is certainly a very daring enterprise to try to guess from an English translation what Pasternak's novel is like; but you know a good deal more about it reading it in English than not reading it at all. And I hope that you may, if not at my hands at least in some happier future, feel that mathematics, though a help, is not indispensable for some insight into the essentials of what has been found in modern physics.

In the second lecture, I shall be talking about quite profound changes in our idea of causality, in what we think of determinism in the natural world, and most of all of what we mean and may mean by objectivity. These changes were necessary in order to attain the prize of a reasonable understanding of the ordinary properties of matter, those properties which manifest themselves even when you are not attacking matter with the violence which the great accelerators and the cosmic rays make possible. And in this lecture I want to discuss some changes in the ideas of space and time. Both of these themes are variations on the problem of the consistency of what we know about motion in space and about what is in space, about its field or content.

The quantum theory was the work of many people. I

think that we would all agree that Niels Bohr was the heart of this brilliant group. On the other hand, the ideas of space and time, though they go back a long way, were revolutionized in this century by one man, and in some aspects at least it is permissible to think that if he hadn't lived, the revolution would not have occurred. He was Einstein.

The first theory of relativity, at least in the Western world, does not date from the twentieth century. It dates from the thirteenth and early fourteenth, from the Paris school of natural philosophers, of whom Buridan and Oresme are the best known. It was certainly one of the great changes in human thought and it is remarkable because, although it is physics, it did not rest on any elaboration of observational or experimental technique but on analysis and on ordinary common-sense knowledge of how things behave. And it was the opening without which the future development of science is hardly thinkable. This was the discovery: in an analysis of the problem of motion, uniform motion—a body moving with constant velocity—was not something for which you could find or needed to find any explanation or cause; uniform motion was a natural state of matter. Of course, this was not the schoolman's view; it was not Aristotle's view, for whom it was obvious that to keep something moving you had to work on it, and the only natural state was one of rest. The new viewpoint was called the theory of impetus, which we would today say was the theory of momentum, namely that the constant impetus of a body was something that needed no explanation and that all you had to explain was change in its impetus, change in its motion, change in its momentum. This, as you know, was also Galileo's view; and we call the transformation of co-ordinates, which emphasizes this cause-less character of uniform motion, the Galilean transforma-

8

tion—although without his permission and without any good historical ground. The idea behind this transformation is that because it involves no cause to have uniform motion there will be a similarity in objects which are in motion with respect to each other. There will be no inherent difference between them. There will be an ability to describe one as analogous to the other. This so-called Galilean transformation tells you how from the co-ordinates x of an object that is at rest at a time t, you can derive the co-ordinates, the time, and the velocity as seen in a system in which that same object moves uniformly with a velocity v.

$$x' = x + vt,$$
$$t' = t.$$

Suppose you have something at rest and it's at the point x and you are looking at it at a time t. Now suppose you move with respect to it with a velocity $-v$. Then the co-ordinate of the object will be given by x', the time won't be changed, and any velocity V that may appear in the original system will appear as a new velocity V' in the new system, $V' = V + v$. This is the Galilean invariance and it's just common sense. It says the particle simply moves along with its co-ordinate increasing because it is in motion, the time isn't changed by this velocity, and the velocities add. This theory of impetus is, of course, Newton's first law; and Newton's laws of motion, which describe how accelerations are produced by forces, are invariant under this simple transformation. You cannot distinguish one uniform motion from another by the application of Newton's laws; they are relativistic in the sense that relative motion is observable, but absolute motion is not as long as it is uniform, that is with no acceleration.

9

From the time of Newton up to the end of the last century, physicists built, on the basis of these laws, a magnificently precise and beautiful science involving the celestial mechanics of the solar system, involving incredible problems in the Cambridge Tripos, involving the theory of gases, involving the behaviour of fluids, of elastic vibrations, of sound— indeed a comprehensive system so robust and varied and apparently all-powerful that what was in store for it could hardly be imagined. I think the only record I have seen of any explicit doubt on the subject of the Galilean transformation and of Newtonian mechanics was about a century earlier than the theory of relativity in a paper of Euler. Because of the relative transverse motion between a fixed star and the earth, you see the star at a slightly different angle than the true direction. Euler found that he did not get exactly the same result when he calculated this variation from the point of view of the star and the point of view of the earth. The difference was totally insignificant experimentally and he didn't say anything more about it. He just noted it.

But early in the nineteenth century and increasingly through that century another study in physics was under way, not having to do with the motion of bodies under gravitational forces, but having to do with the domain of light and electro-magnetism. It was not necessary—although today it is—to decide whether gravity was an action at a distance in which one body affected another very far away or whether gravity spread from one body to another. And there was at that time and is today no really good experimental way of distinguishing the two. There are, in principle, very good ways and we feel sure that we know the answer, but we have not yet tried it out. However, with electromagnetic forces the situation is quite different. I think you have all seen what happens when you have a simple bar magnet and some iron filings on a piece of paper. The iron filings assume quite regular patterns, following lines which have something like parabolic shapes around the poles of the magnet. Already in the first half of the nineteenth century Faraday knew about this and his vision was that the space surrounding the magnet, although it had no pieces of matter in it, had something which was physically important present in it, and that was a magnetic field: the power to affect a magnet. Of course, the little iron filings act like magnets and are affected and do respond to this field and make it manifest. In the same way if you have an electrically charged rod or ball and if you come into the near-by area with another charged object with the same charge, you will feel it pushed away a little; if you present an opposite charge, you will feel it pulled in a little. And these are things that happen when the two are not in contact: they arise from a property of the space surrounding the electric charge or the magnet. Faraday talked of these lines and tubes of force, of the electric and magnetic potentials—I don't use this term technically—which exist in space, and for him space became animated with these fields. They were things which anyone could measure: one could measure their directions, one could measure their strengths; they were as palpable as the corporeal bodies themselves, but they existed in a vacuum. Indeed, they exist very well in a vacuum, and have nothing to do with the presence of air; they are modified by any matter if it is there, but they are present without any matter. This picture, of course, is beginning to be the famous aether, the empty space that is capable of having properties.

Faraday showed that if you changed the magnetic field rapidly, you would make an electric field and Maxwell discerned theoretically that if you changed the electric field rapidly enough you produce a magnetic field. This effect was later verified; it is much harder to see than Faraday's result, merely because of practical considerations. In fact, Maxwell predicted that, in the absence of any charges and currents, field pulsations of this kind, in which electric and magnetic fields would generate each other, could propagate freely. He calculated the velocity of the pulsations and found that it was a rather well-known velocity—that with which light propagates.

Thus this field of Faraday's is busy. It not only has fields around charges and magnetic poles—magnetic dipoles really—but it transmits electromagnetic waves. It transmits all the waves which feed the television sets and instruct the rockets and give us our wonderful culture over the radio; it transmits light, it transmits heat; it transmits many forms of very high energy radiation—forms of light which are very penetrating, which play a big part in nuclear physics. (The reality of man-generated long wavelength electromagnetic waves was established late in the last century by Hertz.)

This highly peopled space, full of electric and magnetic phenomena, is related to particles in motion in the following way: if I have a charged object it will, of course, respond to gravity (a universal force), but it will also respond to electric fields and if it is in motion it will respond to magnetic fields. It will feel a supplementary push, the electric field pulling it in the direction of the field, and the magnetic field in general pushing it at right-angles to the field, and to its own velocity. The laws of these effects on charges were reasonably well known at the turn of the century, at least for objects that did not move too fast. But what was very troublesome is that Maxwell's account of the propagation of electromagnetic waves of light and the whole basis of his theory and Faraday's intuitive picture of a space filled with fields was not consistent with the Galilean invariance property.

One can see this from a general viewpoint for, if this space is full of electric and magnetic fields, it need not appear at all the same thing when I move with respect to it. More specifically—and this is really the crux of the difficulty—according to Maxwell's theory the velocity of light is something that is fixed by his equations. His result was very close to the observed measure. But if I move with respect to the medium in which these fields are described by Maxwell's equations then I would expect to apply the formula $V' = V + v$, that the velocity which I see for the light is the sum of the velocity with which I am moving (or its negative) and the velocity of light in the medium; it might be bigger or it might be smaller, depending on whether I am moving towards the source of light or away from it. This is a view which was indeed prevalent at the turn of the century, and which was shown by many indirect methods and one very direct experiment, one of the great crucial experiments in history, to be simply not so.

Before this experiment, the situation presented at least three alternatives. First, one might say that there is a system—the system in which electric and magnetic fields are described and exist and obey Maxwell's equations—which is unique, and absolute rest has meaning by reference to that system, and anything in motion with reference to it may have different physical behaviour because of this motion. To accept this alternative is to give up the invariance law and to give up the whole idea of relativity, that is the relativity of uniform motion. The second possibility was to say that Maxwell's equations, in spite of their describing such an enormous range of phenomena, may somehow not be right, and this was extremely hard to do after a half-century of success. And the third was to say: 'There is relativity and Maxwell is right, but the Galilean equations don't describe the transformations of relativity'. No one could do that until the situation got really desperate.

And it was made desperate by the Michelson-Morley experiment. In preparing for these lectures I looked up Einstein's lectures in 1921 at Princeton; he said of the Michelson-Morley experiment: 'I assume its results are known to you.' I thought I should not quite do that because it was done a long time ago. What Michelson did was to measure the time taken by light to move a moderate distance back and forth in the laboratory and to see whether this was the same when parallel to the earth's motion round the sun and per-pendicular to it. The expected differences were quite small, and it took a very great technical virtuosity to be able to look for them. But Michelson did the experiment and he did it over and over again. Now, the earth might just possibly be in the preferred rest system of electromagnetic phenomena in January, but then in June it is moving in a very different direction, and with substantial speed; Michelson's sensitivity was enough to have detected very very easily the motion of the earth, by the change in the velocity of light depending on whether the earth was moving with or against or not at all in this luminiferous aether, the seat of electromagnetic pheno-mena. He got a null result. This was so unexpected that the experiment, with many refinements and variations, was repeated for decades after that as a witness to the traumatic character of this answer.

So we are not allowed to believe that the velocity of light depends on the velocity of the source. We are not really allowed to doubt that Maxwell's equations are true in all co-ordinate systems and we are not really allowed to doubt that the equations of the Galilean transformation are not a good description—they are only an approximate description—of what happens when we observe a system that is in uniform motion with respect to us. At this point three people found the solution, but only one found its full meaning right away, and that was Einstein.

Einstein said: 'Let us imagine what the situation would be if we could not communicate with a speed greater than a light signal.' That is pretty fast (3×10^{10} centimetres per second) by ordinary standards; we would not normally notice this limitation. We would not find that our bicycles were getting away from us. But it is a finite velocity, and that makes a very big conceptual change. If you do not have instantaneous communication and if you want to compare information at two different places, you must make allowance for the time it takes for the message to get back and forth. For instance, suppose you want to synchronize two clocks that are a long way apart. (They should be clocks of the same type, perhaps natural clocks which are more or less guaranteed the same—'atomic clocks'.) A natural way to synchronize them so that they read the same time would be to set the clock at one place half-way between the time at which the signal left the other and the time at which it was received back after reflection. The notion of simultaneity, which intuitively seems to be something that should not depend on any moving around you do, is indeed a valid notion when things are at the same point of space, but is no longer a valid notion over substantial distances and when relative motions at all comparable to the velocity of light come into play.

This means that if it is true that you cannot send signals faster than light, and if it is a physical contradiction to imagine it, then you have this relativity of simultaneity, this velocity dependence of judgements of simultaneity. Also you have other physical effects which are produced for you by the machines that you use for measuring distance and for measuring time. Let me explain that when I say 'clock' I mean something that is designed to measure as accurately as possible regular intervals of time, and when I say 'distance' I mean something that you measure with a ruler, which has been by remote comparisons calibrated by a standard metre in Paris. The clocks and rulers then are physical objects.

Now, in order to be consistent with the fact that there is a limiting velocity which is not infinite, but is the finite velocity of light (called by everybody c), the Galilean transformation must be abandoned and replaced by a new transformation called the Lorentz transformation, after the first man who wrote it down. This must provide the co-ordinate of a point x and a time t, when I look at it from a system uniformly moving with a velocity $-v$.

$$x' = \gamma(x + vt)$$
$$t' = \gamma\left(t + \frac{xv}{c^2}\right)$$
$$\gamma = \left(1 - \frac{v^2}{c^2}\right)^{-1/2}$$
$$V' = \frac{V + v}{1 + Vv/c^2}$$

This is a very simple Lorentz transformation; v is the relative velocity of the two systems, and γ is something which is near one when the velocity v is small compared to the velocity of light c and which becomes infinite, marking the limit of the applicability of these transformations, as v

approaches c. Moreover, this clearly indicates the limiting character of the velocity of light. You see that it shows that a length interval in one co-ordinate system will appear to be shrunk by the factor $1/\gamma$ when examined in a moving co-ordinate system. You see that the time is not told the same in the two co-ordinate systems and that the difference not only has a difference of scale but depends on the positions of the clocks. This is the point about the judgements of simultaneity. And you see further that if you have a process going on which takes a time t as measured in the system where the object is at rest, then if you move at a velocity v with respect to it, the time will be lengthened, being γt.

To summarize, motion decreases the measurements of length, motion increases the intervals of time, and the two facts together are encompassed in the Lorentz transformation. Further, the formula for the velocity V' indicates that if you add two velocities that are very close to the velocity of light you never get beyond the velocity of light, you just get a little closer to it. This completely consistent system never enables you to talk about or to discuss the properties of relative motion with a velocity greater than that of light, but it does tell you how to talk about real motions in terms of the actual behaviour of actual clocks and rods and atoms and all the rest of physics. These equations give an invariant description of physical phenomena, a description independent of relative uniform motion, one which is as good in one system as in another. This formalism re-expresses the ancient theme of Buridan, that uniform motion requires no cause, but now with this very new wrinkle that couldn't have been anticipated on the basis of ordinary experience, that, because objects cannot be accelerated beyond the velocity of light, the analogue of an infinite velocity is a finite velocity.

From this viewpoint one naturally asks that not only Maxwell's equations of electromagnetism but the equations of motion for charged particles and then also for neutral particles should be invariant, i.e. that they should have the same content, irrespective of the frame of reference in which we describe the phenomena, as long as we are talking only about uniform motion. We do that naturally in talking of ordinary things. If there is a complete symmetry in a problem, so that no direction is singled out, then we certainly would like to talk about it in such a way that that symmetry is preserved in our description; and if there is nothing in space to make one point different from another, we would like to give a description which is as valid in Chicago as it is in Hamilton. And in the same way here we would like a description valid irrespective of the relative velocity of the objects we are talking about and what we ourselves happen to be doing while we are looking at them.

This was done for mechanics and gave at once the rather clear sign that Newton's equations are wrong. This is clear *a priori*, because if the acceleration is proportional to the force and inversely proportional to the mass, there is no reason why you cannot make velocities bigger than that of light. Something must prevent those forces from being so effective, and what it is, to put it a little oversimply, is that the mass of a body is not in fact constant. Indeed, if the theory of mechanics is to be compatible with the requirement of the constancy of the velocity of light and relativity in this restricted sense—the mass of a body must increase with its velocity in just this way:

$$m = \frac{m_0}{\sqrt{(1 - V^2/c^2)}}.$$

Here m_0 is the mass of the body at zero speed and m its mass at speed V. This is the origin of much fertile speculation by Einstein, because if the mass of a body increases with its velocity so does its kinetic energy and it will increase in the same way, viz:

$$\Delta T = c^2 \Delta m.$$

The symbol ΔT means the change in kinetic energy and Δm represents the corresponding change in mass.

Because the total energy is really something that is not lost or gained by a system, but is conserved, what is true of kinetic energy must be true of all energy and, therefore, a change of energy and a change of mass go hand in hand and the change in energy is related to the change in mass by the square of the velocity of light. This is something that it would be nice to have a little mathematics or more time to show; but it is a direct and really quite inescapable consequence of the purely kinematic connexions which I have written down as the Lorentz transformation.

Another important point is that these transformations mix up space and time very much more than the Galilean ones. To a limited extent you cannot interchange space and time. They have inherently different character. A watch is a watch and a ruler is a ruler and you cannot use the ruler to measure the time and the clock to measure the co-ordinates. But they do change with relative motion. Of course, you are not restricted to move in a straight line with respect to something you are studying: you can also turn around or you can take another place in space. This whole set of procedures—rotation, translation (moving to another origin, that is another base point), and moving uniformly in some direction—together are a set of operations that are closed and form the Lorentz group. You cannot, with these operations, convert any space-like interval into a time-like interval or any time-like interval into a space-like one, but you can change the 'direction' of a space-like interval and give it some slightly more time-like quality, and you can do the same thing for time-like intervals.

This system, this special theory of relativity, which predicts correctly the behaviour of rods and clocks under motion, became an absolutely all-pervasive feature of physics. We use it literally in almost every branch of nuclear physics and many branches of atomic physics, and in all branches of physics dealing with the fundamental particles. It has been checked and cross-checked and counter-checked in the most numerous ways and it is a very rich part of our heritage. For instance, many of the particles that are produced in the atmosphere by cosmic rays are unstable. They have a natural tendency to come apart into others, to decay. But if they move very fast, their decay rate is slowed down and the rule is simply:

$$\tau' = \tau(1 - V^2/c^2)^{1/2} = \tau/\gamma$$

where τ is the decay rate when the particles are at rest and τ' is the decay rate when they are moving with speed V. This is observed and is a very vivid thing. We have not yet seen people stay young, but we have seen particles stay young by the billions.

There is another point, a little out of chronological order. I have spoken of rotations, translations, and uniform motions as part of the Lorentz group, but there is another part of the Lorentz group that is not so simply connected with these operations. You cannot rotate your right hand into your left. The only way you can get the one to be congruent to the other is with a reflection in a mirror. You may try wiggling your hands about, but it is really not possible to rotate one into the other. One would think that if rotation did not make any physical difference, reflection would not either, that if space were so isotropic that there was no direction singled out in it, then it would not matter if something were right-handed or left-handed. The two arrangements would be equally probable—there is a good deal of this accidental character in human asymmetries. This invariance law was believed for at least thirty years. Many many brilliant examples turned up where you could classify the states of atomic and nuclear systems according to whether they were unaltered by reflection or whether their symbols changed sign under reflection; in both cases you may say that to any allowed motion or phenomenon in physics, the mirror image also is allowed. If you can have something happen with a wheel turning a certain way and an arrow pointing up, then keeping the wheel the same, but reversing the arrow, which is what happens when you hold up a mirror, will also be allowed. Such objects do exist in physics; in fact the neutrino is a very good example of one. It is only a few years ago that some doubt arose as to whether this rule was strictly true—the rule, that is, that to any system found in nature, the mirror image must occur, being compatible with the laws of nature. The doubts were sufficiently anxious and deep that Lee and Yang looked into it and found that no proof of this rule had been really given experimentally in a certain class of very feeble forces and very slow reactions. And so they looked— not they but their friends—and the answer is that nature has, in this special manifestation, a most violent and total preju- dice in favour of right-handed and against left-handed arrangements and the other way round in other cases. It is very odd, very unexpected, and possible only because you cannot get from a rotation or a translation to a reflection. What we now more or less believe is that if any configuration is allowed, then if you take its mirror image and replace all the positive charges by negative and vice versa, and let it run backward in time, that will also be allowed. But that is all we are really confident we know.

This theory of relativity has been very much mixed up in all the developments of physics. I would stress that the odd and often seemingly paradoxical things that are embodied in the special theory of relativity are not paradoxes in the sense of being conflicts between different experiments. They do not involve any contradiction on the part of nature; what they do involve is a gross change, a rather sharp change, from what learned people and ordinary people thought throughout the past centuries, thought as long as they had thought about things at all. The simple facts, namely that light travels with a velocity that cannot be added to or subtracted from by moving a source of light, the simple fact that objects do contract when they are in motion, the simple fact that processes are slowed down when they take place in motion, and very much so if they move with velocities comparable to the velocity of light—these are new elements of the natural world and what the theory of relativity has done is to give coherence and meaning to the connexion between them. These contractions of objects and these retardations of events are, of course, reciprocal; and that is a little paradoxical. It is a little hard to think that, if a moving chunk of matter gets flatter and flatter in the direction in which it is moving, and if you happen to be with that chunk of matter, you would get flatter and flatter if you looked at yourself where you originally were. But it is true; and the same kind of thing is true about time; this is the origin of the twin paradox. It is true also that when there are changes in mass, there is in practical terms a corresponding enormously big change of energy, as we know, both to our hope and our caution. We are not sure that in approaching the domain of the very small (and I am here not now talking of ordinary atomic dimensions, but dimensions some million times smaller), we know exactly what it means to say that 'nothing' can move faster than light. But we are sure that our doubt is not with moving faster than light; our ambiguity is with 'nothing'—we do not quite know what that means in this domain.

I come now to a generalization of the theory of relativity, which starts when you begin to think about motions which are not uniform, and goes on to consider the nature of gravity. General relativity has very very few connexions with any other part of physics and, as I said, is something that we might just now be beginning to discover, if Einstein had not done so more than forty years ago. This is partly because, compared to electricity, gravity is a very weak force and really manifests itself only when you are dealing with bodies that are pretty substantial, such as the earth, the sun, and smaller things, but not on an atomic scale. Consequently, it is rather inaccessible to experiment, because the objects you deal with are big and not things you can wiggle around very much. You might think that gravitation should resemble electricity in producing fields which exist in the vacuum, which can be measured, and which propagate with the velocity of light. Something like this is true, but there are two enormous differences. One sign of a difference is that like charges repel each other, like masses attract, and this means the two cannot be really quite the same. Another is that gravitation is a quite universal phenomenon; all bodies follow the same pattern when they are acted on only by gravity: this was Galileo's principle of equivalence.

However, if you follow out the attempt, and this has only been done in the last year or so, to make a theory for gravity as much like the theory of electricity and magnetism as you can, you find that, quite apart from the rigorously predictable effects of uniform motion on the measurement of space and time, gravitational fields have much deeper and much more tangled effects on the behaviour of rods and clocks.

If you study this further, you have to come to two conclusions, that in important ways gravitation is a very different thing from electricity and magnetism. First, the rods and clocks are so affected that the space that they measure out, which is always flat if you look in a small region of space in a small interval of time, manifests over bigger regions curvature like the surface of a two-dimensional egg. This curvature may vary from point to point and is itself an expression of the gravitational effects which are in this space. And second, because gravitation, like electromagnetism, involves potential energy and because gravitation is produced by all mass, and therefore, by all energy, gravitation produces gravitation and gravitational fields are not linear in the sense that if you have two gravitational waves they do not merely superimpose their effects, but they interact. Also, if you have a gravitational wave and a gravitational field around the sun they interact. All of this can be found out in a sort of pedestrian way by making the analogy with electricity and magnetism.

But for Einstein it was entirely different. He came at it from two points. One was the universality of motion in a gravitational field which enabled him to think that this might be a geometric thing. The second was the fact that the principle of relativity, philosophically, ought not to be limited to uniform motion. If there is nothing else around, how can you tell if something is being accelerated or not? You can only tell that by reference to something that is not being accelerated. But we know that accelerated motion differs from uniform motion in that we do not have to be told when we are undergoing it, because we feel it and phenomena do respond to it. Einstein observed that a uniform acceleration is exactly the same thing as a uniform gravitational field in all its physical effects. This is another principle of equivalence. And he, therefore, was led to the idea that the problem of dealing with non-uniform motions and the problem of explaining gravitation were related and indeed identical.

If you are moving in something resembling free space you really cannot tell how fast you are moving unless you refer your motion to something else, to the earth or the sun or the stars. But if you are moving in a jerky way, if you are being made to move faster, being accelerated or slowed down, you can have all the blinds drawn, you cannot know where anything else in the world is, but you still can tell that something is going on and you can measure it. And, therefore, there can be no elementary possibility of talking about general motions, motion on a circle, motion which speeds up and slows down, motion on a bumpy railroad train being relative, because within the moving thing (this railroad car or elevator or rocket) you can tell by the way you feel, and you can look at gauges to measure that you are being pushed, pulled, hauled around, jerked, whatever it is. One could, therefore, say that relative uniform motion is indeed relative and no law of nature must discriminate in favour of one such motion rather than another, but that the elementary fact about accelerated motions is that, at least in the part of the universe where we live, we can tell whether we are being jerked around or not, and such motion is not relative. Nevertheless, Einstein's theory of accelerated motions is called the general theory of relativity; it is a very unfortunate terminology. One might almost say that this should be called the general theory of un-relativity, except for one clue, a very deep clue, that was known before, but was understood and made very prominent by Einstein.

If you are confined to a box from which you cannot look out and in which you can make only internal measurements, and if you feel a uniform acceleration, you cannot tell whether you are being speeded up by some force acting directly on the box, or whether you are feeling a uniform gravitational field. The simplest way to confirm this is to fall freely and notice that when you fall freely there is no gravity and there is no acceleration; you are, in fact, accelerating, and you are, in fact, in a gravitational field, but the two of them cancel. You should not achieve this state by jumping out of the window, but if you ride in airplanes enough it will be done for you. Therefore, Einstein understood that one could deal with a more general class of motion only if one also encompassed the phenomena of gravitation. I should say that this principle, that gravitational fields and accelerations are in large measure equivalent to each other, is often called the equivalence principle. It is closely related to Galileo's principle that if the only forces involved are gravitational, all bodies move in the same way. If Galileo's principle were not so, you would not be able to replace gravitation by an acceleration which clearly is the same for all bodies. In the way Einstein did this, the theory of gravitation and the theory of general motions were indissolubly linked.

But one could go about it in what appears to be a more straightforward way, and, in recent years, this less beautiful approach has been developed. One could say that gravitational forces, like the electromagnetic forces, are long range, in that they fall off slowly with distance, and that this suggests that one make a theory of gravitation, which is a natural analogue of the intuitive pictures of Faraday and the equations of Maxwell which describe electromagnetism, electromagnetic waves, and the fields around magnets and charges. The principal point of difference for which one must allow from the beginning is this: that two like charges repel each other, whereas all masses attract each other. If you do this you get a description which reproduces Newton's theory of gravity if fields are not phenomenally strong—and there may be no strong gravitational fields in the world—and if in addition they don't change rapidly with time so that the finiteness of the limiting velocity (of light) plays no part. In this theory one has both principles of equivalence, both that of Galileo and that of Einstein. And one has some famous physical consequences which also were predicted by Einstein. For instance, both theories predict that when light falls in a gravitational field it turns bluer; it turns from red to blue, as frequency increases, and the wavelength decreases. The most precise and, I think, by far the most beautiful example of this is a recent experiment conducted at Harvard in which light was simply allowed to fall down from the third floor to the basement of the Physics Building. One could see how much bluer it had become: one part in 10^{14}: not very much. Also, as Einstein predicted, and as had been guessed before, light is deflected when it passes through a gravitational field, near the sun, or, for that matter, near a star. And you also find, as I have already mentioned, that a gravitational field induces more gravitational field, unlike the standard case of light.

Finally, and perhaps most importantly, if you develop this analogy between gravitation and electromagnetism, you find one very major and deep difference. This is the point where really to explain where the difference comes in would take not a little, but a lot of scribbling on the blackboard, but to explain what the difference is, I think, does not. I shall use the word 'space' to mean both the three-dimensional space that we usually mean and the extension in time which we have learned to see is not sharply and totally separable from spatial intervals, because they get mixed up when you look at things in uniform motion. You find that if you explore space with ordinary rulers and clocks, this real space is not the space of Euclid, it is not the space of the classical geometers, but it has some structure and some distortion built into it. This is not the space you imagine on paper; it is the space which you measure, typically, with rods. Now it is very hard to think, at least for me, about four-dimensional continua, especially when one of them is not a distance but a time, but it is legitimate to think of an ordinary two-dimensional surface and suppose that the four-dimensional affair is just a mathematically similar abstraction—just as easy to discuss mathematically but much harder for people to visualize. Then what we have been saying is that we are not dealing with the analogue of a plane surface, but with the analogue of something curved in a rather peculiar way. Locally, in a small enough region, any curved surface, if it has no ridge in it, is flat and it looks like a plane; but if you move along it for some distance, the inherent distortion of the space becomes clear; for instance, the sum of the angles of a triangle will not be a straight angle and Pythagoras's theorem will not be true, and all sorts of geometrical complications will be induced. When you have a sufficiently vigorous and wild gravitational field, such distortions will occur in the nature of space and time, and can be detected by actual measurement. From this it then follows that if you accept the gravitational analogy of electromagnetism you are led to things that have no parallel in electromagnetism; and, if you have your eyes open, you reach Einstein's theory, or something very like it and close to it.

But Einstein, forty-five years ago, did not do this. He developed his description of gravity on the basis of a few rather general ideas. One is that gravitational forces are determined by matter and express themselves in the geometry of space and time. Now, what are the determining aspects of matter? Not its colour, for example, but those aspects that are most clearly related to its mass, energy, momentum, or impetus and related things which form a unitary description of matter. I should say, in this context, that electricity and magnetism, because they have energy, also contribute to gravitational fields. The second important point is that the inherent properties of the geometry wholly determine the gravitational forces that act on bodies. We use the word 'inherent' to stress that we are not concerned with how you describe the geometry in terms of co-ordinates, but with those properties which constitute the structure of space and time. So that you have on the one hand that the inherent geometry is determined by the distribution of matter and, on the other, that the response of matter to gravity is determined entirely by the geometry. In fact, matter moves as nearly in a straight line as the crinkly character of the geometry permits. These are the two basic points of Einstein, but they would not lead to anything very definite. In a way which is quite characteristic of physics and which will recur later in these lectures, Einstein also had in mind limiting situations where he knew the right answer. One was the gravitational theory of Newton, which is right, as I said, when fields do not vary too much with time and when they are not overwhelmingly strong. The other is that space and time, if you look at a sufficiently small region, must be flat, and in such a region must be described by the Lorentz space of special relativity.

Those are four elements, we may say four of Einstein's postulates; and the fifth one is the one that nobody can ever translate: the theory must be a simple thing. And here it seems to me we really are faced with the fact that only by inventing the right notation and using the right mathematical ideas can you say whether something is simple or not. With a good deal of fumbling, and many years of unsuccessful trying, many years in which the physical ideas which I have just outlined were clear, Einstein finally came upon a branch of mathematics that other people had made and which gave him the perfect vehicle for writing down how it goes with gravitation and what the general theory of relativity is. And no one today, plodding along to remake this theory along more pedestrian lines, can fail to be overwhelmed by the imagination, the daring, and the beauty of what Einstein did. It is a very different thing to say whether this is a correct theory.

It is, of course, correct in all those particulars which I have talked about, but there is very little experimental evidence about the features of the theory which are peculiar to it, and which have nothing in common with electromagnetic theory, with flat space time, or with Newton's theory. We may be a long time wishing that we knew, but I have never known a physicist who did not think that it was probably a very very good guess indeed. And there is not a shred of evidence against it. We have for space and time not finished with the story. What will come is not my business to try to say, but on two fronts there are wide-open questions.

One is on the scale of the very big, encompassing everything that we see with telescopes and that we hear with radio telescopes. That means more than the distance that light can travel in five or ten billion years, which is about where the present limit lies. We see the universe flying apart; we do not see anything very detailed about its spatial structure. And it is a completely open question, not answered now and conceivably never to be answered, whether the volume of space (I am not now talking of time) is a finite or infinite thing. Einstein thought it was finite, but that was because he thought that everything was steady and static. When we look we see that the motion is the characteristic feature; the further away we look, the faster things are receding from us, and in such a world we have no insight into whether this will stop and there is a finite distance to look or whether it will go on for ever and ever.

Another kind of open question I referred to earlier, and that is that when we get to dimensions so small that they are not of the size of atoms, not even of the size of nuclei, but of the size of those objects of which nuclei and atoms are composed, we cannot really be sure to what extent we can discriminate near-by points in space and time and to what extent the designation of such points is still meaningful. But I will say one thing. Here there is no question of curvature of space because gravity is an utterly negligible force, and we assume that here, too, the velocity of light is a finite limiting velocity imposed on all physical disturbances or signals. From this assumption a great deal can be made to follow, and, so far, nothing that follows from it has shown itself to be in conflict with experience. It is one of the powerful tools of modern-day physics.

II. Atom and Field

The subject of my lecture tonight is really the quantum theory. It has two parallel and even complementary historical origins. One is from the properties of electromagnetic radiation, but from other properties than those which were important for relativity. The other is from an attempt to understand the structure of atoms. I mean by the structure of atoms the atoms of the chemist and the spectroscopist, and not the atoms of the physicist who works with a giant accelerator and who smashes everything that he looks at with his violent collisions. This subject is also interesting but it has been opened up really only in the last decades, and is not understood, whereas the quantum theory was very much a complete theory thirty-five years ago.

As to the properties of electromagnetic radiation, I need first of all to come back with a little more than just words to the idea that a changing magnetic field makes an electric one, a changing electric one makes a magnetic one, and that this pumping cycle produces an electromagnetic wave. These waves have certain important, deep, but rather abstract properties, in common with everything else that physicists call waves. A typical electromagnetic wave may have the electric force changing with time periodically, so that it is sometimes positive and sometimes negative, that is, sometimes pointing, let us say, in the positive direction, sometimes in the negative, and going through zero as it changes from one to the other; the magnetic force is doing the same thing at right-angles to the electric force and out of phase with it, so that when the electric force is zero the magnetic force is a maximum, and the whole thing is travelling at right-angles both to the electric force and the magnetic force with the velocity of light. That is one kind of electromagnetic wave and for us it is plenty.

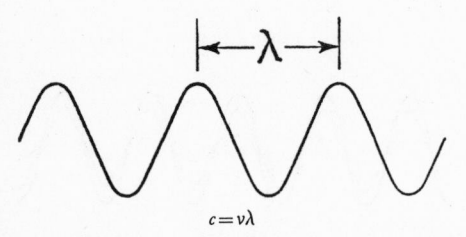

$$c = \nu\lambda$$

Such a wave is characterized by three numbers: the wavelength λ, the frequency ν, and the velocity. The wavelength is the distance from crest to crest of the wave, that is the distance from one point where the electric field is a maximum to the next point at which it is a maximum. The frequency is the rate at which the electric field changes with time at a given point. The product of these two is the velocity of the wave—for an electromagnetic wave, this is the velocity of light, and we write $c = \lambda\nu$. More generally, we can define in a similar wave the wavelength and frequency for a sound wave, or a water wave, and their product is the velocity of the wave, that is the speed of sound and the speed of progress of the crest of a water wave respectively.

Now the important part of a wave motion, which is true of electromagnetic waves, sound waves, or water waves, and is indeed very easy to observe with water waves, is that if you have two waves more or less in the same part of space and time, they affect each other so that the disturbances add. For example, the electric field that comes from having two electromagnetic waves is the sum of the electric fields of the separate waves; so is the magnetic field. That means that I may have

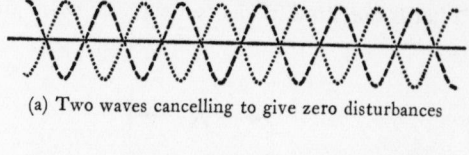

(a) Two waves cancelling to give zero disturbances

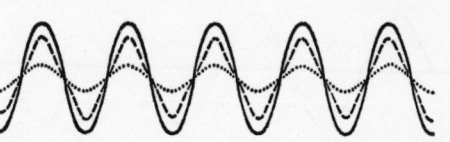

(b) Two waves adding to give a disturbance larger than either

do sound waves?

No

another wave that is added to a given one in such a way that the electric fields add or in such a way that they cancel, depending on how they lie with respect to each other. An important point is that the intensity of light or electromagnetic radiation, the energy it carries, and many of the effects it produces are proportional not to the electric field but to its square. Looking at the diagram, you see that waves can interfere with each other both by adding and producing twice the height of the wave and therefore four times the intensity, or destructively, according to the upper curve (a), so that where one wave is big and positive, the other wave is big and negative, and you get zero for an answer. These are the general phenomena of waves which I need to presume, I hope not wholly irresponsibly, that I have told you about, and which we shall be using all evening in our discussion. We must

34

remember that these properties are true of all waves—water waves, sound waves, and all electromagnetic waves, from those that one uses for the longest wave radio transmission through microwaves, through heat, through light, through ultraviolet light, through X-rays, and up to the highest frequencies there can be.

One consequence of this wave property is that light which comes through different paths may interfere and I will give just two examples of that; one of which we will have to return to.

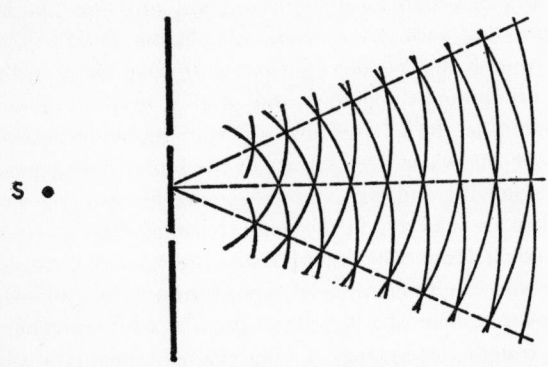

The sketch shows a source S, a diaphragm with very thin slits in it, and out of these slits diverging waves of light. The curved lines represent the crests of these waves: where the crests coincide you will have particularly intense light; where the crest and a trough coincide you will have none at all. You see that the presence of the two slits gives rise to a pattern of brightness and darkness, which either slit alone would not explain and which is characteristic of the wavelength and the separation of the slits. If there were a large number of slits, all spaced the same distance apart, then light would only move in certain directions from this collection of slits, which is called a grating, and these directions are simply related to the ratio of the wavelength and the separation of the slits.

Now, a century of experimentation showed how beautifully the phenomena of the propagation of light—its reflection, its passage through slits, its diffraction from gratings, its dispersion—could be explained in terms of these simple ideas of the interference of waves. There is not to this day the slightest doubt that this is a correct description; it is used every time a radar antenna is designed and any time that one really wants to deal with electromagnetic radiation and its propagation around objects; the light or radio waves from different gaps are brought together and give a resultant intensity depending on the relative phases of the interacting waves. In this case the waves are abstract in the sense that there is no matter moving and, by Chapter I, no aether moving either; but they are concrete in the sense that there are electric and magnetic fields, the ones that Faraday dreamed so much about, which you can measure; every one of these crests corresponds to a measurement of a big electric field at a certain time, and every trough corresponds to a big magnetic field at a certain time. (These measurements would be extremely tedious to do with light, but with long radio waves it is a straightforward experiment that does not teach you very much, but confirms your sanity.) Now, it was exactly at the turn of the century that this harmonious picture of the nature of electromagnetic radiation received a sharp jolt from which it has never recovered. To explain this, it would be easier to skip history entirely, but I will say how Planck discovered it.

When you have a gas of molecules each molecule has, on the average, about the same energy as every other and this energy is a simple measure of the temperature of the gas. If you have electromagnetic waves in an enclosure you can convince yourself that every wavelength should also have about the same energy as every other, and this energy is equal to the temperature of the matter which forms the enclosure and is emitting the waves. This is, on the face of it, absurd, because the theory of relativity says that there can be no limit on how short wavelengths are since all you have to do to make them shorter is get on a fast train, and they will be shorter. Therefore, there will be an infinite energy content to any piece of space that is allowed to come into thermal equilibrium. Energy would simply drain out of matter and everything would be absolutely cold, because all the energy would go into the electromagnetic field. This, it was known, is not true. In struggling to find out why, Planck had a very great advantage. He knew that, for very low frequencies of the light waves, this rule that all the light waves in the enclosure had the same energy was right. He knew that for very high frequencies something quite different happened, and the energy that a wave had was the energy that would be required if one had to create a quantum of energy given by the expression $h\nu$. He introduced the constant h to connect these two régimes which had earlier been studied; it has always since been called Planck's constant. It is, as you see, a constant which, when multiplied by a frequency, gives one an energy, and it will recur; it is the signal, the mark, of atomic physics and is called the quantum of action or Planck's constant. Planck was able to derive a formula which reconciled this behaviour of the equilibrium properties of the enclosed radiation, and also to determine a reasonably accurate value of his constant, but only by employing the technically possible assumption that light was not emitted continuously as a wave should be, but only in energy packets, which correspond to a multiple of the frequency, viz. $h\nu$. He did not believe this, and for many many years struggled to get his formula without making this dreadful assumption which contradicted the whole idea of light as a wave. Because here it was being said, not that light was emitted, like radio waves, simply by charges moving around, but that light was emitted in a whole single operation with a unit of energy, and if that amount of energy could not be emitted, nothing happened; if that could be emitted, it happened; if it could happen more than once, it happened more than once. Well, in this very statistical and complex and dark area it was possible to suppose that Planck had made a mistake, and he lived for years in the confident hope that he had made a mistake.

But he was wrong; and a great blow was struck to his hope when, in the same year that Einstein made the special theory of relativity, he made another paper, which was to prove even more mischievous. The second paper is very closely related to Planck's discovery. If you shine light that is not too red on a metal surface, electrons, which are part of the metal, will come out of it. The very odd thing which had been found in the laboratory was that if you shine the light twice as strongly it does not affect the velocity of the electrons; rather, it affects their number. But, of course, if you are thinking of light as an electromagnetic wave and the wave is more intense, you would expect that the electrons would have more work done on them. But not at all. The energy of the electrons is unrelated to the intensity of the light, but very simply related to the frequency of the light and to Planck's constant.

$$E = h\nu - B$$

The light energy $h\nu$ is the same energy that Planck had

38

$$c = \lambda \nu$$
$$E = h\nu$$

frequency

$$\nu = \frac{\varepsilon}{h} \qquad c = \frac{\lambda \varepsilon}{h} \qquad \frac{1}{c} = \frac{h}{\lambda \varepsilon} = \frac{1}{c} = p\varepsilon$$

$$\frac{1}{p\varepsilon} = c \qquad \frac{1}{p m c^2}$$

introduced five years earlier, E is the energy of the electron as it moves away from the metal and B is not fundamental: it is the work that you have to do to get the electron out of the metal in the first place. This formula has been very accurately and beautifully confirmed. And Einstein said: 'This clinches it. Obviously there *are* units of energy in light.' When light is absorbed by an electron, it happens in multiples of these units $h\nu$, and then the energy is simply carried off by the electron and that explains the formula.

But, of course, this did not do away with the century of experiences on wave phenomena. Interferometers and prisms, microscopes and radio waves still studied light in terms of the propagation of waves. On the other hand, here was this discontinuous particle aspect, at least to phenomena in which light was absorbed or emitted, which could not be laughed away. Moreover, this was even confirmed by experiments with very hard light, viz. X-rays. In fact, when they collide with electrons, they act as though they had the energy given by $E = h\nu$ and a momentum, or impulse, $p = h/\lambda$, which is just h, the same constant, divided by the wavelength. Thus one could see that light acted in collision with electrons like a particle with a momentum and an energy related to its frequency and wavelength by these very simple rules, consistent with the rules connecting energy and momentum for an electromagnetic wave, but involving both this constant h, and a discrete transfer of energy and of momentum from light to electron in a collision between the two. This experiment, called the Compton effect, had led to a very serious and critical view as to the dual nature of light by about 1923.

Probably the situation could not have been readily understood had it not also been compounded by another and equally puzzling aspect: this time not directly the behaviour of light,

D

$$\frac{1}{m\nu \cdot mc^2} = \frac{1}{m^2 c^2}\nu = c$$

$$\frac{1}{pm} = c^3 \qquad \frac{1}{m^2\nu} = c^3 \qquad \frac{1}{m\sqrt{\nu}} = c^2$$

but the behaviour of matter on an atomic scale. Let me remind you that, just before this century, Thomson discovered the universal ingredient of ordinary matter, the negatively charged electron which is very light compared to the atom, some 1/2,000th as heavy or less, and which has the unit of charge which we find uniquely throughout the atomic world. Thomson rightly imagined that the number of electrons in an atom was connected with its chemical properties and its place in the periodic table, so that atomic hydrogen would have one electron, helium two, uranium—92. He knew the atoms were neutral, but he did not know where the neutralizing positive charge was; and his best guess was that it was probably extended over a volume of the order of the size of atoms, that is a sphere 1/100th of a millionth of a centimetre in diameter. This was the Thomson model of the atom, and it raised no problems, because it was a rather vague model, and you could not do very much about it. But Thomson was able to show that some regularities, like the occurrence of regular numbers and periods, such as occur in the periodic table, might be expected from such a model. However, this model did not last long, because of the work of Rutherford, which started at McGill, continued at Manchester, and was finally brought to fruition there. Rutherford showed that positive charge of an atom was not spread out over atomic dimensions.

How he did this is itself very beautiful. He had been studying naturally radioactive radiations, coming from uranium, radium, and related heavy elements; he got their family relationships straight and decided which chemical elements were produced by the natural decay of which other elements and which disintegrations followed which; he had distinguished three types of radiation: positively charged and heavy, which were the nuclei of helium and which he called alpha-particles; negatively charged, and light, which were electrons; and neutral, which were very high frequency light. He did not at first know that alpha-particles were helium nuclei, but he thought they were, and he became interested in what happened to them, as they passed through matter. They did not do what they would if atoms had a uniform smooth positive charge, and very light electrons located within it, as suggested by the Thomson model.

In that case there could never be a big force to deflect the alpha-particle, because the smooth charge does not have sufficiently concentrated electricity and the electrons have much too little mass to knock an alpha-particle around, for it is 7,000 times as heavy. But he found that indeed the alpha-particles were, not often but regularly, deflected through very big angles indeed, and from this he concluded that the positive charge was concentrated, and that it was concentrated, along with most of the mass of the atom, in a region with dimensions smaller than 1/10,000th of atomic dimensions. And so he discovered the atomic nucleus which has the positive charge which gives the atom its chemical and most of its physical properties.

This was a marvellous story, but it was only the beginning of really very great puzzles. Think of the simplest of all such atoms, the hydrogen atom. It has a proton, one nuclear particle, at the centre with a unit positive charge, and somehow there is an electron associated with this to make up a system which has a well-defined size. The size is standard; unless the hydrogen atom has been through a wringer or been hit over the head, it always is the same. And it emits a certain characteristic batch of colours when you bash it. Not one of these properties could be intelligible on the basis of Newton's ideas about motion and the idea of how charged particles affect each other, because Rutherford had proved that the field around the proton was the electric field. This field is in its form exactly like the gravitational field around the sun: the forces fall off with the inverse square of the distance and they all point towards the proton, for in this case they are attractive, since the electron and proton are oppositely charged. Consequently, it is just the problem of the planetary motions all over again. Now, one obvious thing that we know about planetary motions is they can be more or less anything: any ellipse, in any plane, with any eccentricity, and any size. Therefore, it is most odd that all hydrogen atoms should have the same size and act in the same way. There is no trace in classical physics of any reason why each hydrogen atom should not be of a different size and shape and behaviour than the next or any other.

Furthermore, although I have not gone into this in detail, we know that if we have a charged particle describing a circular or elliptical orbit, it is accelerated, and an accelerated charged particle will make light waves and lose energy. But hydrogen, unless it is bashed, does not do anything of the kind. It can sit for years and centuries quite content without ever changing. It does not lose its energy and the electron does not spiral in and disappear into the nucleus. And finally the laws relating the colours of light that are emitted from such a classical orbit are a little more complicated, but similar in form to the laws determining the sound frequencies produced by a violin string. There will be a fundamental which is connected to the period of revolution of the electron in the orbit and there will be overtones or harmonics, i.e. multiples of this frequency; whereas the observed frequencies for atomic spectra, hydrogen included, are not harmonics or integral multiples of a fundamental frequency, but rather complicated arrangements of differences between numbers which are not harmonically related. To be specific all the observed frequencies can be written as

$$\nu = \nu_i - \nu_j$$

when ν_i and ν_j are two of a sequence of numbers ν_1, ν_2, ν_3 .... In the case of hydrogen, these numbers had been recognized by Balmer, and in general they characterize the atom in question. In other words, the uniqueness of atom systems (which is harder to prove, but just as true, for an atom with 92 electrons) expressed in the law of the light emitted when they are excited, their stability, and the fact that they are all the same size, had no roots in any then existing piece of physics. This was the very great predicament which caused Bohr to make one of those wild guesses which even his own great caution was unable to keep from looking very revolutionary. Bohr said: 'For reasons which we don't yet understand, an atom is not characterized by classical orbits, but it is characterized by a set of states which are essentially stationary, which don't change in time.' Of these the most familiar and important is the one with the lowest energy, the ground state, and that lasts for ever, unless the atom is disturbed. These states have different energies and those which have more energy than the ground state may not be stable; a transition may occur from such a state to a lower one spontaneously. We remember that each frequency emitted from a given atomic species can be written as $\nu = \nu_1 - \nu_2$, and we may make this into an intelligible equation by multiplying it by h, Planck's constant:

$$\mathcal{E} = h\nu = h\nu_1 - h\nu_2.$$

Then each term in this equation is an energy, and we could assume that the two quantities, $h\nu_1$ and $h\nu_2$, are the energies of

43

two states in the atom, and the quantity $h\nu$ is the energy of the quantum of light that is emitted in the transition between them. 'I cannot', said Bohr, 'describe these transitions. They are not motions in any classical sense. They are something new that I don't understand.' Bohr went on to say: 'I can give you a rule, in some cases, for I calculated the energies for these states, and this I can do in terms of the properties of the corresponding classical orbits.' But Bohr did *not* say, and this turned out not to be true, that these states have anything in common with orbits. For one thing, an orbit is a motion and something changes with time. The stationary state is just what it says: it does not change with time at all.

We have now reached the crisis of quantum theory; but before we get through with this story we will see that we have a vast extension of our idea of intelligibility in science, that we have a vast generalization of what we mean by objective knowledge, and that we have a much better analogue to the human predicament than could possibly have been built on Newtonian physics.

Our crisis arose in two studies which, it turns out, are very closely related. The first was the discovery that, although all electromagnetic waves, including light, are described so perfectly as wave phenomena showing interference and giving diffraction patterns, nevertheless, in their transactions with matter, they have a discrete character, behaving like light quanta, with definite energy and definite momentum, and that they negotiate with matter by giving up this energy, or by taking it from matter or by colliding with matter in an elastic collision. Secondly, we had the problem, created by Rutherford's discovery of the atomic nucleus, of what in the dickens the electrons were doing in the neighbourhood of the nucleus. They were not moving on planetary orbits, they were not radiating, they were not behaving like a small solar system; but they were, for the most part, in stationary states, essentially stable, the lowest one completely stable, as Bohr said. When they moved from one state to another, this was not a motion which could be pictured in space and time; but the energy difference between the energies of the stationary states could appear in a form of radiation, the corresponding light quantum. There were rules which were not precise and not generally applicable and which I shall not write down, that Bohr gave for identifying the energy of these states.

Bohr knew that this was a radical departure and an incomprehensible one and he immediately followed it up with a suggestion very much like that which guided Einstein, namely that this new scheme, which seemed so wild and unfamiliar, must, in some situations, reproduce the world we knew. Those situations were ones in which very highly excited states of the atom were involved, in which many stationary states were involved, and where the discreteness of the stationary state and the finiteness of Planck's constant would not make very much difference. This he called the 'correspondence principle'. The new theory must describe the world of Newton and the world of Maxwell when we are away from the discrete elements that characterize the quantum theory. This principle turned out to be a most powerful tool; and by 1925 it had been possible to write down laws not involving any image of motion, not involving any clear connexion with Newton's laws or with particles in orbits, but laws which nevertheless were generalizations of Newtonian mechanics and which directly described the connexion between transitions between atomic states and the properties of the atomic state themselves.

I am glad that it did not stay at that, because this is very hard to explain without mathematics. I think my first paper dealt with a simple problem of a molecule with two atoms by this machinery, but it was very hard to interpret what this was about and very hard to solve problems. The solution which most of us find easiest to explain and which is in fact identical with that which the 'correspondence principle' led to, came in a very different way. It came in a wild idea that was very soon generalized and verified, and the wild idea was that there should be a wave associated not just with electro-magnetism, but also with every kind of particle in nature, specifically with an electron.

These waves are not electric and magnetic disturbances; what they are I will say in a minute. But the relations which characterize the connexion between the wave prop-erties of light and its energy momentum were preserved, viz:

$$E = h\nu$$
$$p = h/\lambda.$$

I have used the same letters, ν and λ for frequency and wave-length, E and p for energy and momentum. This was proposed by de Broglie, who was able to show that one could get a plausible account of the stationary states of the hydrogen atom by the requirement that those states would be realized in which standing waves could be established which were in resonance, that is where the number of wavelengths in the circumference of the Bohr 'orbit' would be an integer. This was pretty shaky and it was thoroughly disbelieved—I believe his paper was refused publication. Nevertheless, it was right, and within a year one had found evidence that electrons are indeed in some way wave-like, because they show inter-ference and they diffract just as light does and just as X-rays do.

Also within a year, one found a less sketchy way of describing the relation between the propagation of these waves and the simple forces present in something like a hydrogen atom, where the electron is simply subject to the electric attraction of the proton. This universal wave-particle duality immediately did several things. It explained the existence of stationary states, not as orbits, but as something new with no analogue in classical theory, as things which indeed were steady in time. But they were not static in this sense! If you measured the kinetic energy or the average square momentum of an electron in a stationary state it would not be zero, but it would be the same at any time as it was at any other. It would not change in the course of time. A close connexion between the properties of these waves and Bohr's 'correspondence principle' was very quickly set up. But I will not turn to these questions, which are a little mathematical, but rather to the way in which the discovery of the universality of wave-particle duality gave a clue as to the relations between the wave aspects and the particle aspects of light and of all matter. It is also true that a brick is associated with a wave, but it is not a useful thought, because the brick is very much bigger than its wavelength, and we shall never see the interference effects that correspond to macroscopic objects.

The wave-particle duality refers to an individual event and that is a very very striking thing. Let us think again of our two slits. The source may be a light source, or it may be an electron source. The interference acts between the crests of the waves to produce a bright spot in the pattern, or destructively between a crest and a trough to get very little light. This not only describes what happens when you have a lot of light coming from a source, but it describes perfectly well what happens when the light is very faint and you expose a photographic plate for a long time. It describes, in other words, the behaviour of individual quanta of light or individual electrons leaving the source. That fact tells us that the relation of the wave to the finding of the particle is a statistical one: where the wave is strong, we are likely to find the particle, and where the wave, because of destructive interference, is weak, we are unlikely to find it. More than that, the reconciliation

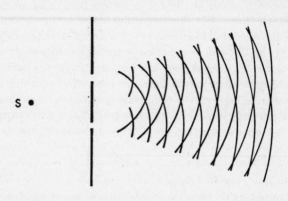

of the wave-particle problem involves the following considerations. If you think of this experiment in terms of a light quantum going through one of the slits and being affected by the other slit through which it does not go, you are led to an impossible description of nature, because then things which are not involved in an experiment may affect the outcome. Thus, our presence here tonight may affect the outcome of an experiment in the reactor building a little away; such an idea has no end. The point then is this: in such a set-up you will observe the interference of the light or the electron waves passing through the two slits (or in the more general case, you will get the unidirectional character of light transmitted through a long grating of slits), but you will only do so as long as you leave the experiment as it is with no attempt to find out through which hole the light or the electron passed. Once you arrange to have a little spring in one of the slits, so that when the light is bounced on that slit you notice it, you will have destroyed the interference pattern and you will get only the pattern that you would have if that slit, and that slit alone, were open. How can this be?

It can be because not just the light and the electron, but the slits themselves have the character of being represented by a wave field. Now a wave field, however abstract it may be, has the property that if you want it concentrated in a little region of space you must have different wavelengths present which will reinforce each other in that region of space and cancel outside it. If Δx is a dimension of the region of space, there must be a spread of wavelengths $\Delta\lambda$, such that

$$\Delta(1/\lambda) \gtrsim \frac{1}{\Delta x} \; ; \; \Delta\lambda \gtrsim \frac{\lambda^2}{\Delta x} \; ;$$

the smaller the region in which you wish to confine the disturbance, the larger must be the spread of the wavelengths. But if you look at this formula, and remember that $p = h/\lambda$, you will see that there must be a spread of momenta involved. Indeed, the equations show that $\Delta p \Delta x \gtrsim h$. In words, the spread in momentum multiplied by the spread in position cannot be less than the quantum of action, Planck's constant. This result is true for the light, for the electron, for the slit, and for anything else that you want to study. This provides a completely consistent restriction on how you may and how you may not use the idea of wave and the idea of particle. The restriction is consistent, because it is universal in that every measuring instrument that you use is as limited in its ability to define at the same time both position and momentum as is the object that you are studying.

In actual fact, these waves represent not electric or magnetic fields, but a state of information. They represent what you have learned by an experiment. Suppose, for instance, that you set out to determine that light passed through the upper slit, or to determine that it was monochromatic light emitted from the source. These two complementary measurements are, in fact, mutually exclusive, because by the time that you had detected the passage of the light through the slit, you would have allowed it to collide with a slit in an effective manner, and thereby to destroy your confidence as to its colour (which is essentially its wavelength). The colour would have been changed by the collision. These waves have a well-defined relation to statistical prediction in that, as in the case of light, their square determines the intensity, which in this case is the probability of finding the particle, either light quantum or electron. They also represent in a general way the kind of information which you can obtain about an atomic system, whether it be its momentum, its position, its energy, or any other possible kind of study you may wish to make of it.

In deciding what measurement is possible, we must take into account the fact that not only the system, but everything we can use to observe it with, is subject to the limitation of complementarity, of which this uncertainty relation between the definition of the momentum of a particle and the definition of its position is the most famous and the most fundamental example. If you have an atom, the stationary states are not orbits. To produce orbits you must take a whole mass of stationary states and build up the waves in a suitable manner by adding the waves of stationary states. So an orbit is complementary to a stationary state; you can realize one or the other, but if you do one, the other is foreclosed. It is also the same with a light quantum; you may have a probability wave for a light quantum, and that is what we have been talking about here; but if you want to build up an electromagnetic wave you must have many light quanta and you must superimpose the waves from many light quanta to make a good old-fashioned electromagnetic wave such as we send and receive. We know that there are indeed many quanta in such waves.

The important point is that it is not merely that we do not always know everything that in classical mechanics we thought we could know, like the position and momentum of an object; if that were so, you could say: 'Well, I know its momentum and I will suppose that it is distributed somehow over different possible positions and I will calculate what I'm interested in and take the average.' But you must not do that. If you suppose that an object whose momentum you have determined by experiment has a distribution in positions, no matter what the distribution, you will get the wrong answer. It is not that you do not know it; it is that it is not defined. The experiment which gives you the momentum forecloses the possibility of your determining the position. If you welch on it and say, 'Well, I want to know the position in the first place', then you can, but then you lose the knowledge which the earlier experiment had given.

One is thus led to a view that a good, well-designed observation gives information. This will determine a wave field, and this wave field develops in time in a quite causal way. That is, if you know it at one time its future will be also known. From this wave field, by taking its square, you can determine the probability for the outcome of another experiment at the future time. These predictions have been checked and checked and checked, and in some wonderful cases are right to one part in ten billion, or something like that. When you make your new observation to check the prediction you generally, but not always, render the old wave function no longer a reasonable description of the system. You also have wild situations in which you may use one particle to study another and in which, depending on what you do with the test particle, you may produce a state for the other which either has a well-defined momentum, or a well-defined position. You cannot do both and you exercise your option by what you do with the observing particle rather than with the observed particle. This gives in a most vivid way a notion of how limited the objectivity of an atomic system is, because apart from a description of what you have done to study its properties, it is not logically possible to assign properties to that atomic system. You cannot say: 'I think it is in this part of space and maybe it has such and such a velocity. Let me try it out.' You have to take into account, in order to give it any properties at all, what you have done to observe it or what you know of its history. In other words, you have to take into account the relation of this object to the world of nature, not to you as a human being, but to you as one of the many physicists who are in the game.

This theory is, therefore, one which has forced us to a quite different notion of what we mean by objectivity. All over the world, in France, in Japan, in New Zealand, in communist countries, we talk about atomic physics, and we check each other's experiments. In that sense it is a most objective part of our knowledge, and a most well-verified one. These comparisons are possible because we can tell each other how we have gone about an experiment and what we saw and what we found. Mistakes are made, but they are found very quickly. The objectivity which we see in this is not a characteristic that you can look up in a book, it is not an ontological characteristic of the atom at all. It is a characteristic of the way we can talk with each other about it, of the lack of ambiguity and of the reproducibility and the verifiability of our communication with each other.

Quantum theory is, of course, an acausal theory in the sense that events happen for which no precise cause can be determined or given. A given nucleus disintegrates at three o'clock on the afternoon of a certain day. No one in the world could find out when that would happen until it did happen, but he could give a law saying how many in 100,000 nuclei of the same kind would disintegrate in any interval of time. It is a non-determinist theory. There is no possibility, as there was in Laplace's nightmare, of knowing everything about the world right now—not a very plausible assumption—and therefore knowing all about its future—not a very happy outcome. In every experiment, in atomic physics, you look at something, or have other ways of knowing something about the system; it develops according to laws of wave propagation which are simple and well known; then you look again and you get an answer. Everything about this is quite different from the Newtonian picture. You are free in your choice of what you are going to look at to begin with. You are free in what question you ask later; but the event itself is unique. You can try it again and it will not in general give the same answer, because the connexion between the two experiments is a statistical one, not a necessary one.

III. War and the Nations

I have been discussing the idea of complementarity: that it is impossible to measure precisely two complementary aspects of a physical system. Always when you talk about an atomic system it may be big, it may be a crystal, it may be a nucleus, it may have billions and billions of atoms in it, but always it is a finite part of the world; and in order that you can make an observation of it, you must use the rest of the world for the machinery with which you do it. Especially Bohr has pointed out the analogies between this situation of complementarity and familiar traits in life. He has had, I think, a double purpose: one to illuminate the situation in physics and one to reinforce our interest in complementary aspects of human life.

A favourite one is this. When I write with the chalk it is part of me and I use it without any separation between it and my hand. When I look at it and get interested in what it is and put it under a microscope, it is an object of study. I can do one or the other, but the effective doing of one obviously forecloses the effective doing of the other. I may, as we all have to, make a decision and act or I may think about my motives and my peculiarities and my virtues and my faults and try to decide why I am doing what I am. Each of these has its place in our life, but clearly the one forecloses the other. We may talk, as we increasingly do, about the physical disposition and chemical mechanisms in living objects, but when we talk about living objects we also need to talk about the purpose for which these mechanisms have been developed and have survived. Both methods of description have a valuable part, to give either up is to impoverish our understanding of life; but they are not things that can be done at once without confusion.

There are many other examples. Perhaps one of the deepest, because it is the most familiar, is that we all encounter situations in our life in which we look at the predicament of a man, a friend perhaps, or a son, and see it in the light of what is good for him and of our love for him. We know that others will look at it in the light of what is just and what is proper in society. We know that the good societies, if there are any, the better societies are those in which this conflict and this dichotomy and this element of complementarity is not too terrible. Still, we all know, because of the tragic quality of life, that it will always be there. Those who have lived through the unravelling of the heart of the atomic paradox as it existed twenty-five or thirty years ago believe that one has come to a vision of the physical world with far more room for the human spirit in it than could have been found in the great mechanism of Newton.

Very soon physicists, pleased with what they had found and enormously armed with new theoretical and mathematical methods, turned to other problems—not just atomic physicists, but their colleagues in chemistry, in mathematics, and in other branches of physics. For instance, very soon after the quantum theory was elucidated one began really to make a theory of the electron, the first fundamental particle, other than light, to be studied in detail. And the positron, the counterpart to the electron, which has the same mass, but opposite charge, was discovered, and detailed studies were

E

made of the beautiful processes of materialization and de-materialization, in which a pair of charged particles disappear to give two rays of light (two gamma rays), or in which two gamma rays collide to make a pair. This is as beautiful an example of Einstein's relation between mass and energy as one can ask for. But then we got into another branch of study which in the end involved us as a community in politics in some sense (I mean it in a good sense—the judgement of the good society, not the winning of an election), and in the great questions of national and political power. This, of course, is not unheard of. Archimedes, in Syracuse, had the same troubles, and Hobbes, ten years before Newton's *Principia*, wrote of them with a dry dispassion. This began to happen very slowly and without anyone seeing it, when, armed with quantum theory and eager to understand, physicists turned their attention not to the behaviour of the atomic electrons around the nucleus, but to the nucleus itself.

This field was very much opened up by two developments. One, which occurred in the same year as the discovery of the positron, was the discovery of the neutron, the neutral in-gredient of atomic nuclei. The second was the design and construction of accelerators, machines for giving to charged particles sufficient energy to overcome the electric repulsion of atomic nuclei, and to get at them and break them up and to see what they were made of and how they reacted. By 1939 we knew quite a lot of how nuclei behaved, of what their stationary states were like, of how they reacted when bom-barded, and of what kind of products would be produced. Although those were the days of small accelerators, a million times less energetic than those now under study, they were good enough to give a very good insight into the behaviour of atomic nuclei. Rutherford was dead then, in 1939. It was he, who, during the First World War, had produced the first artificial transmutation of nuclei, not with an accelerated particle, but with one of his beloved alpha-particles. He went to his death rather doubtful that large-scale energy releases could be practically accomplished on earth, although the energy changes were certainly there to be made. We learned more of this when, on the basis of studies of nuclei and of what the astronomers could tell, it was possible to give a convincing and rather detailed account of some of the principal sources of the energy of the sun and of many other stars in terms of nuclear reactions changing nuclei and releasing energy in the hot central regions of these stars.

Nineteen thirty-nine was the year of fission and was also the year of the outbreak of the Second World War; a good many changes had come to all people, but also to physicists. Early in the 1920s up until the very early 1930s scientists from the Soviet Union were welcome and were frequently found in the great centres of learning in Europe and warm collegial relations were formed then between Russians, Englishmen, Germans, Scandinavians, many of which persist to this day. That was changed, too, in the 1930s. During the 1930s very many men of science, like very many other men, either had to leave or in conscience did leave Germany. Many of them came to Canada, many to the United Kingdom, and perhaps most of all to the United States. Some came from Italy as well. By 1939 the Western world was no longer a suburb of the scientific community, but a centre in its own right, and when fission was discovered the first analyses of what nuclei were involved and what prospects there were for its practical use for the release of energy were largely conducted in the United States. I remember that Uhlenbeck, who was still in Holland, thought it his duty to tell his government about this development; the Minister of Finance immediately ordered 50 tons of uranium ore from the Belgian mining company, and remarked: 'Clever, these physicists.'

Actually it was very largely the refugee scientists in England and in the United States who took the first steps to interest their governments in the making of atomic explosives and who took some steps, very primitive ones, in thinking out how this might be done and what might be involved in it. In fact, we all know that it was a letter from Einstein, written at the suggestion of Szilard, Wigner, and Teller, that first brought the matter to President Roosevelt's attention; in the United Kingdom I think it was Simon and Peierls who played this early part. Bohr remained in Denmark as long as it was humanly possible for him to do so. The governments were busy. They had a war on their hands and certainly any reasonable appraisal would have suggested that radar, probably the proximity fuse, and in principle if not in fact rockets would have very much more to do with the outcome of the war than would the atomic energy undertaking. It started slowly under crazy names like Tube Alloys in the United Kingdom, and Department of Substitute Materials in the United States. When I came into it my predecessor had the title Co-ordinator of Rapid Rupture.

There were really very many questions. Would a bomb work and what sort of a thing would it be, how much material would it need, what kind of energies would it release; would it ignite the atmosphere in nuclear reactions and end us all; could it be used to start fusion reactions? There was also the problem of producing, in industrial processes that had no previous analogue in human history, the very considerable number of pounds of the special materials, uranium and plutonium, of which the first bombs had to be made. By late 1941 an authorization for production was really given. There was an uneasy co-operation between the United Kingdom, Canada, and the United States, later substantially to improve, but never, I think, to become completely free of trouble, especially for our friends from the United Kingdom, though we learned much and gained much from all their help. There was also, of course, very much secrecy.

Late in 1942 we decided that we must get to work on how to make bombs themselves. On July 16th, 1945, early in the morning, the first bomb was exploded. It did a little better than we thought it might. One of the guards said: 'The long hairs have let it get away from them.' That day, the President of the United States, the Prime Minister of England, and Stalin were meeting in Potsdam. I believed, because I was told by Dr. Bush, that the President would take the occasion to discuss this development with Stalin, not in order to tell him how to make a bomb, which the President did not know, but to do something that seemed important at the time, to treat the Russians as allies in this undertaking and to start discussing with them how we were going to live with this rather altered situation in the world. It did not come off that way. The President said something, but it is completely unclear whether Stalin understood it or not. No one was present except Stalin's interpreter of the moment and the President, who does not know Russian. But it was a casual word and that was all.

The bombs were used against Japan. That had been foreseen and in principle approved by Roosevelt and Churchill when they met in Canada and again at Hyde Park. It was largely taken for granted; there were questions raised, but I believe there was very little deliberation and even less record of any deliberation there was. And I would like synoptically,

59

briefly, on the basis of my memory of the time and of talk with many historians who have grappled with it, to tell you what little I think about this. I think first of all that we do not know and at the moment cannot know whether a political effort to end the war in the Far East could have been successful. The Japanese Government was deeply divided and stalemated in favour of war. The dissident part of the Government had made an overture through Moscow to the West. Moscow did nothing about it until Potsdam. Stalin told Truman about it. Stalin did not seem interested, Truman did not seem interested, and nothing happened. This was at the very time when the test bomb was successful and a couple of weeks before the bombing of Japan. The actual military plans at that time for the subjugation of Japan and the end of the war were clearly much more terrible in every way and for everyone concerned than the use of the bombs. There is no question about that; and these plans were discussed with us; they would have involved, it was thought, a half a million or a million casualties on the Allied side and twice that number on the Japanese side. Nevertheless, my own feeling is that if the bombs were to be used there could have been more effective warning and much less wanton killing than took place actually in the heat of battle and the confusion of the campaign. That is about all that I am clear about in hindsight. That, and one other thing: I am very glad that the bomb was not kept secret. I am glad that all of us knew, as a few of us already did, what was up and what readjustments in human life and in political institutions would be called for. Those are the days when we all drank one toast only: 'No more wars.'

When the war was over, the great men of physics spoke quite simply and eloquently, Einstein in advocacy of world government and Bohr, first to Roosevelt and to Churchill and to General Marshall and then finally quite openly, when nobody else listened but the public, of the need to work for a world which was completely open. He had in mind that we had some very great secrets and that we ought to be willing to relinquish them in exchange for the disappearance of secrecy from all countries and particularly from the secret-ridden communist societies. Stimson, who resigned as Secretary of War in September 1945, wrote: 'Mankind will not be able to live with the riven atom, without some government of the whole.' Among many reports that we in our innumerable commissions produced, I remember two. One of them, which remains, I think, to this day Top Secret, ended roughly: 'If this weapon does not persuade men of the need for international collaboration and the need to put an end to war, nothing that comes out of a laboratory ever will.' The other said: 'If there is to be any international action for the control of atomic energy there must be an international community of knowledge and of understanding.'

All of this was very deep and genuine and I think most of our community, and many other people also, believed it desirable. It was not exactly what Stalin wanted. And it really was not anything to which any government became very clearly or deeply or fully committed. In the absence of a practical way of getting there, the most that could be done was to put forward some tentative and not entirely disingenuous suggestions about the control of atomic energy which, if accepted, would have led in the direction of international collaboration and in the direction of a suitable beginning of world order. That is not how it has worked; and I remind you only of two obvious things. We are in an arms race of quite unparalleled deadliness—I think this is not the place to speak about the amount of devilment that is piled up on both sides, or about the precautions and the difficulties of making sure that it does not go off; on the other hand, we have lived sixteen and a half years without a nuclear war. In the balance, between the very great gravity of the risks we face and the obvious restraints that have seen us through this time, I have no counsel except that of sobriety and of some hope.

It may seem wrong to speak of this as an experience of physicists. It certainly is not an intellectual challenge like that out of which the theory of relativity was born or that which gave rise to the solution of the paradoxes of wave-particle duality and the quantum theory. I doubt if there is a certain specific right idea to be had in the field of how to remake the world to live with these armaments and to live with our other commitments and our other hopes. But it is true that we have been marked by our deep implication in this development, by the obvious fact that without physics it could not have happened, and by the heavy weight which has been laid on so many members of this community in counselling their government, in speaking publicly and in trying above all in the early phases to find a healthy direction. I do not think that even our young colleagues, tearing away at the new unsolved problems of fundamental physics, are as free of preoccupation for their relation to the good life and the good society, as we were, long ago, when we were their age.

There have been, as you know, many deep and painful conflicts among technical people, and I think one can pick up the paper almost any day and find examples of learned men calling their colleagues liars. We are torn by conflicts, and this, I think, was not openly and clearly true in 1945 and 1946. The arms race, the Cold War, the obduracy of the political conflict, and the immense and complex and terrifying scope of the technological enterprise are not a climate in which the simple discussion of physical problems finds very much place. But more than that, of course, these are not physical problems and they cannot be settled by the methods of science. The question of what our purpose is on earth, the question of how we may make a government that will represent these purposes, the question of what our own responsibility is, the question of what business it is of ours to think about these things, are not to be solved in any laboratory or settled by any equation or any mathematics. Part of the conflict among technical people is like the conflict among all people: it comes from conflicting assessments of what our antagonist's course may be, what his behaviour will be—a subject rich in mystery, even for the experts. Part of it comes because we are talking about a world in which there is no relevant previous experience. No world has ever faced a possibility of destruction —in a relevant sense annihilation—comparable to that which we face, nor a process of decision-making even remotely like that which is involved in this. Those of you who have been in battle know how tangled, unpredictable, and unamenable to prior planning the course of a battle often turns out to be, even when it was well planned. No one has any experience with warfare in the nuclear age. These are some of the reasons for acrimonious differences as to what fraction of a population may survive if you do this or do that, or what you may trust our antagonists to do and what you must suspect them of doing. In addition, the community of physicists is certainly no more than any other free of evil, free of vanity, or free of their own glory; we must expect rather ugly things to happen and they do.

But I would really think that on a few rather deep points which do not imply the answers to all the questions in which we could rightly be interested, we are as a community really rather clear as to what our duty is. It is, in the first place, to give an honest account of what we all know together, know in the way in which I know about the Lorentz contraction and wave-particle duality, know from deep scientific conviction and experience. We think that we should give that information openly whenever that is possible, that we should give it to our governments in secret when the governments ask for it, or, even if the governments do not ask for it, that they should be made aware of it, when we think it essential, as Einstein did in 1939. We all, I think, are aware that it is our duty to distinguish between knowledge in this rather special and proud, but therefore often abstract and irrelevant, sense, and our best guess, our most educated appraisal of proposals which rest on things that in the nature of the case cannot yet be known, like the little cost of some hundred million to build a certain kind of nuclear carrier. We think that it is even more important, and even more essential, to distinguish what we know in the vast regions of science where a great deal is known and more is coming to be known all the time, from all those other things of which we would like to speak and should speak in another context and in another way, those things for which we hope, those things which we value. Finally, I think we believe that whenever we see an opportunity, we have the duty to work for the growth of that international community of knowledge and understanding, of which I spoke earlier, with our colleagues in other lands, with our colleagues in competing, antagonistic, possibly hostile lands, with our colleagues and with others with whom we have any community of interest, any community of professional, of human, or of political concern.

We think of these activities as our contribution, not very different from those of anybody else, but with an emphasis conditioned by the experiences of growing, increasing under-standing of the natural physical world, in an increasingly tangled, increasingly wonderful and unexpected situation. We think of this as our contribution to the making of a world which is varied and cherishes variety, which is free and cherishes freedom, and which is freely changing to adapt to the inevitable needs of change in the twentieth century and all centuries to come, but a world which, with all its variety, freedom, and change, is without nation states armed for war and above all, a world without war.